Printed and Published in Great Britain by D. C. THOMSON & CO., LTD.,
185 Fleet Street, London, EC4A 2HS.

- BARNEY -

- CUDDLES and DIMPLES -

- BANANAMAN -

- GROWING PAYNES -

- SHERMAN -

- KORKY the CAT -

ISBN 0-85116-555-9

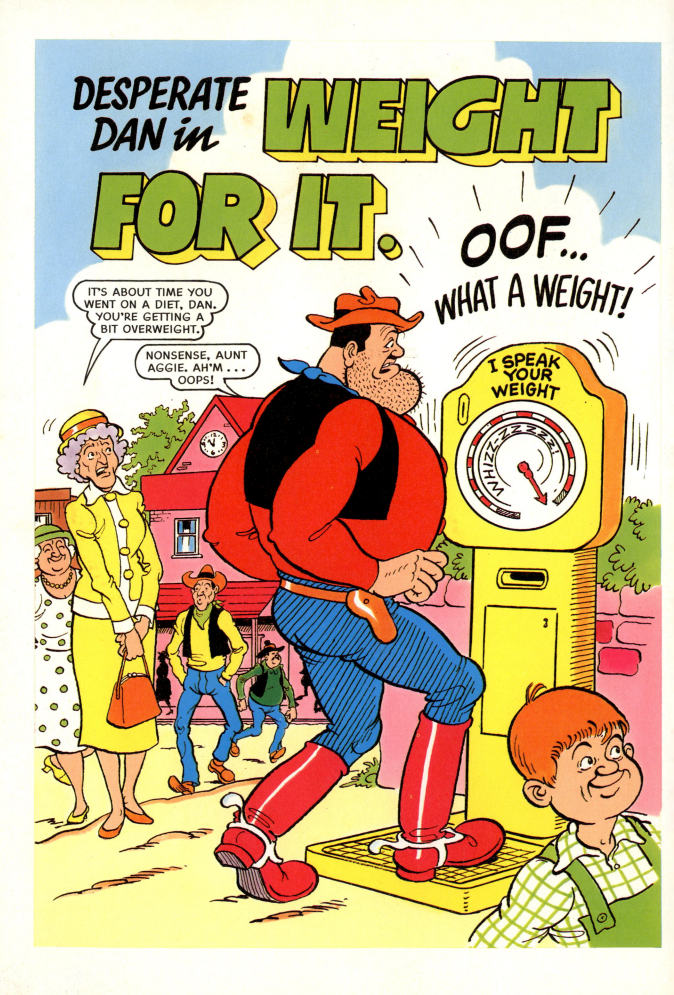

SMITTEN

One brush-up later —

HEY! I COULD DO A PORTRAIT.

And —

LET ME CAPTURE YOUR BEAUTY ON CANVAS, KATIE.

OOH! THAT SOUNDS LOVELY, SMITHIE.

I'LL MAKE YOU AS FAMOUS AS THE MONA LISA.

WHERE DOES SHE LIVE?

But —

HM! THIS ISN'T VERY EASY.

CAN I SEE IT?

WAAGH! YOU'VE MADE ME LOOK LIKE A MONSTER, YOU MONSTER!

TAKE THAT! YOU COULDN'T PAINT OUR CEILING.

Later —

WERE YOU A BIG HIT AS A PAINTER, SMITHIE?

DON'T ASK!

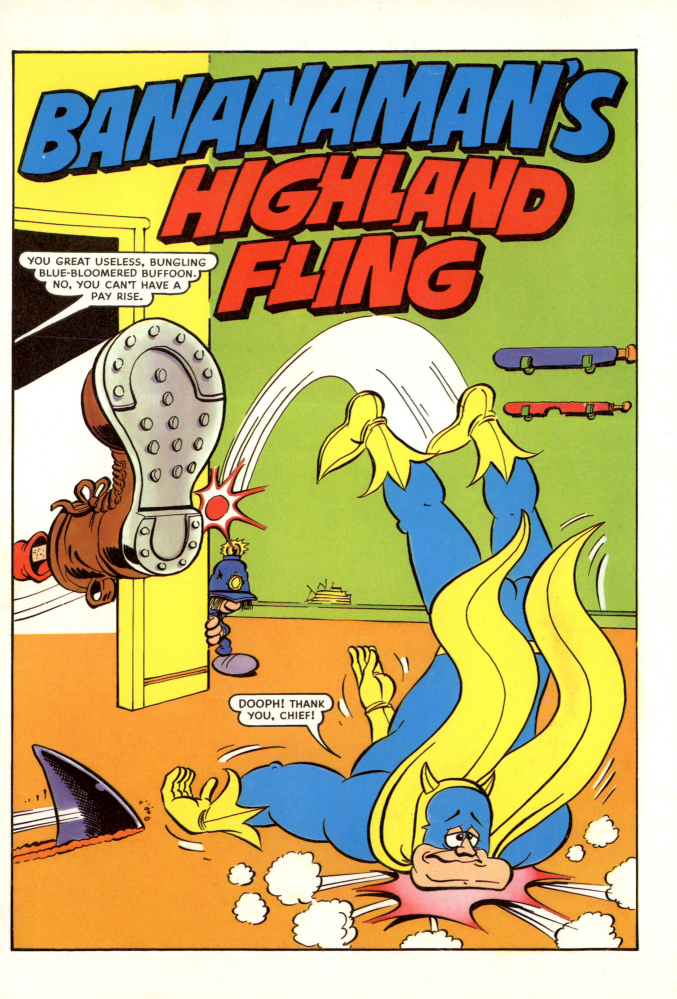

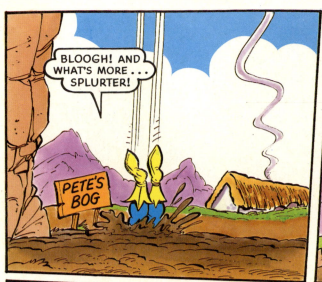

Strange Hill School

WONDER WHAT KIND OF DAY IT'S GONNA BE?

WOWEE! IT'S BEAUTIFUL!

PERFECT FOR OUR CRICKET MATCH!

But—

WHERE'S YOUR CRICKET GEAR, WOLFIE?

WRONG KINDA WEATHER, EDDIE!

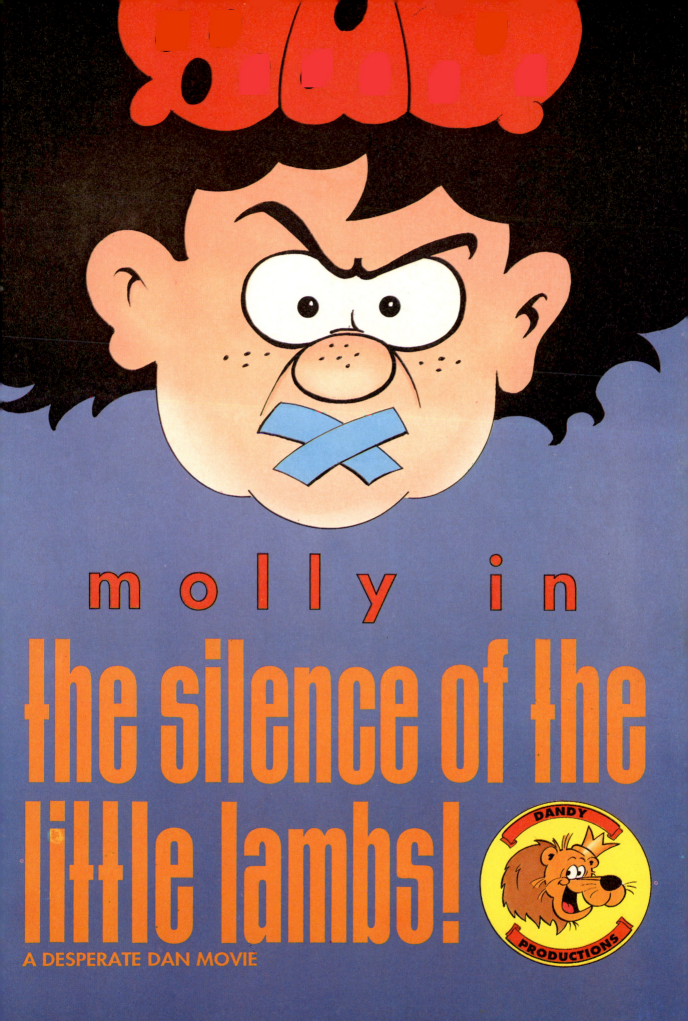

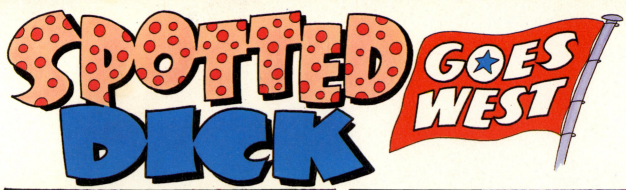

ELMER'S PUT ME UP IN THIS POSH NEW YORK HOTEL FOR A COUPLE OF NIGHTS.

Later —

COME IN!

KNOCK! KNOCK!

HI, DICK! I GOT WORD YOU'D ARRIVED.

HOW COME? I WAS JUST GOING TO PHONE YOU.

JUST LOOK OUT THE WINDOW, SONNY BOY.

Then, at Mount Rushmore —

WOW! WHAT A BUNCH OF BIGHEADS.

And finally at a Hollywood party —

SWOLLEN

SIMPER

LET'S GET ARNOLD WHATSISNEGGER'S AUTOGRAPH!

Time to go home —

I'LL WRITE TO YOU IN A WEEK OR TWO, DICK.

SMASHING! NEXT YEAR I'LL SHOW YOU ROUND ACCRINGTON.

Presently —

JAMES
THE WORLD'S WORST SCHOOL BOY

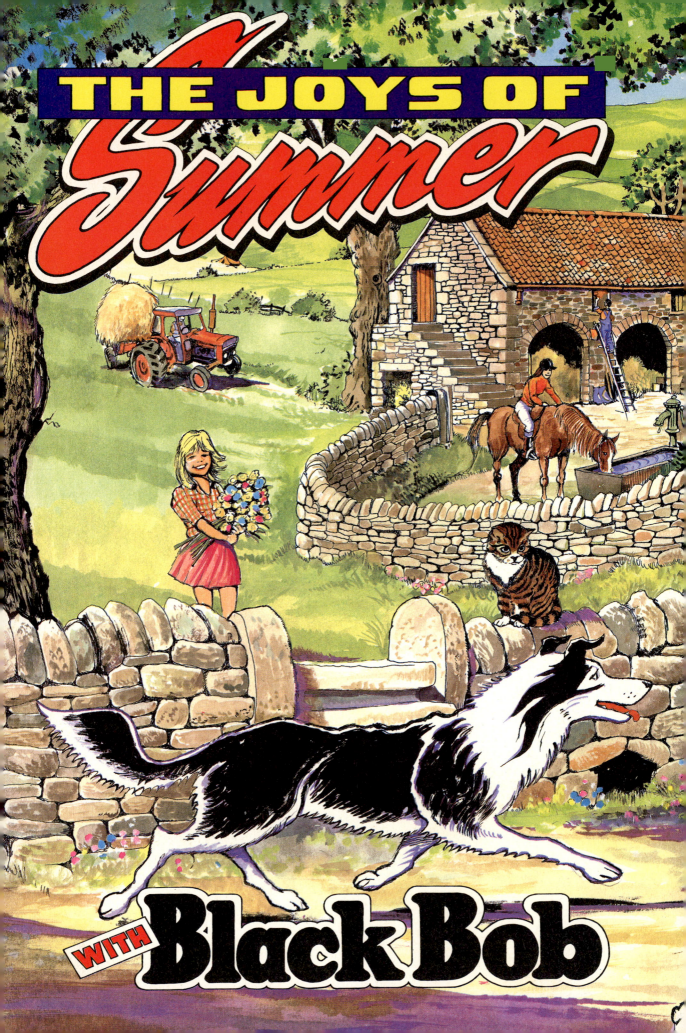

THE JOYS OF Summer

with Black Bob

KORKY THE CAT AND THE KITS.

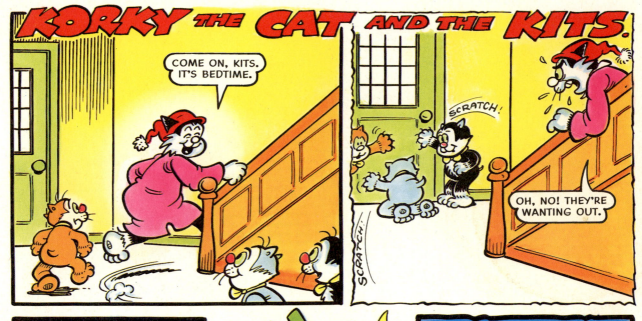

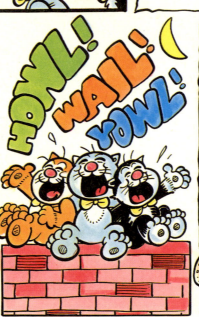

DESPERATE DAN in—
THE BAD SAMARITAN

GOOD DEED WEEK
HELP YOUR NEIGHBOUR
BE A GOOD SAMARITAN

TOWN HALL

THAT SOUNDS A GOOD IDEA. YES, INDEED!

Just then —

BAH! I CAN'T SEE THE TIME ON THE CHURCH CLOCK WITHOUT MY READIN' GLASSES.

DON'T WORRY, NEIGHBOUR.

GONE!

CAN YOU SEE THE CLOCK NOW, OLD-TIMER?

HUH! WAIT A TICK.

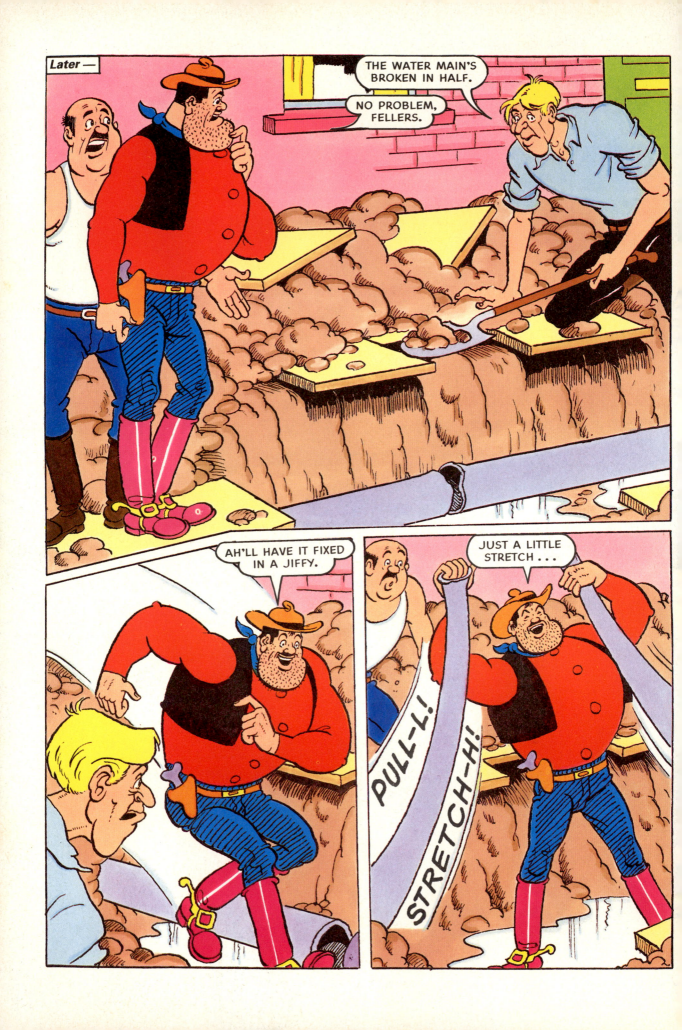

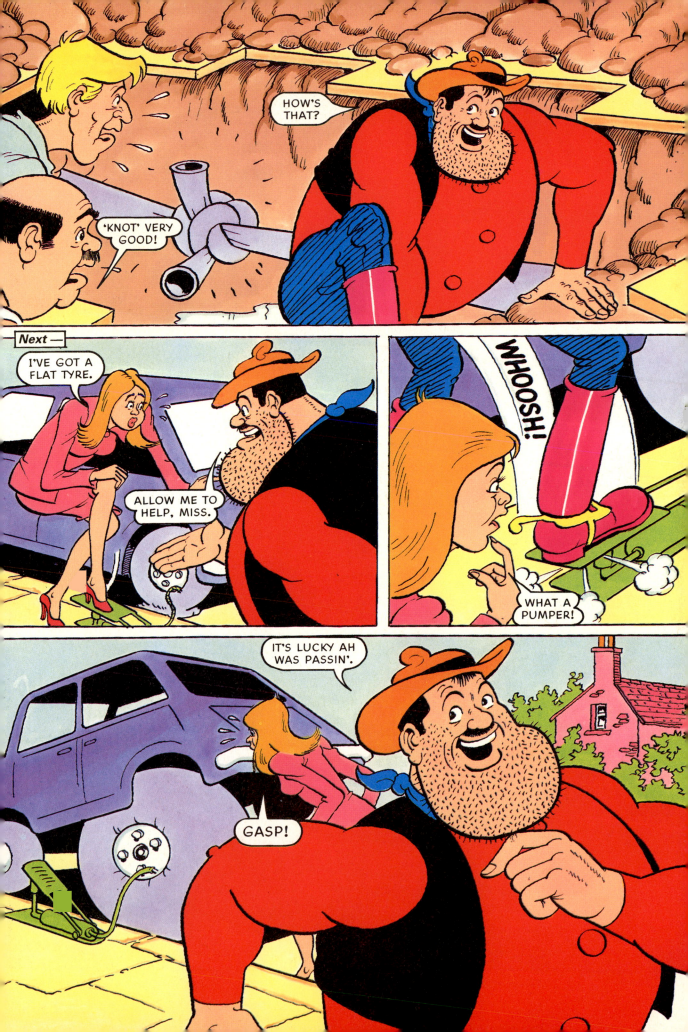

BILLY GREEN
AND HIS SISTER JEAN

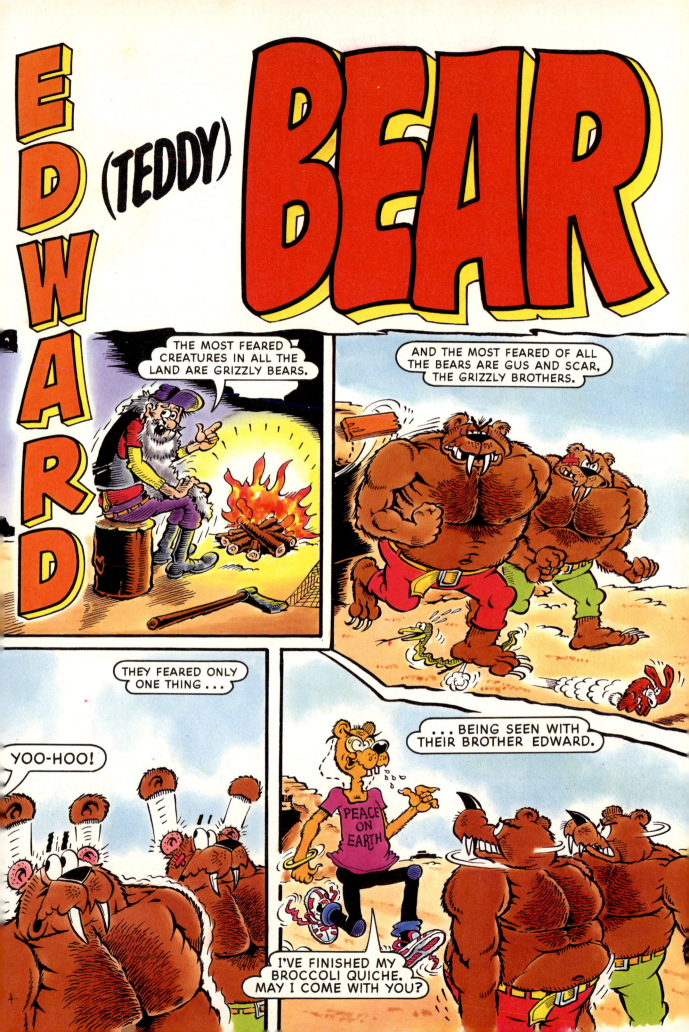

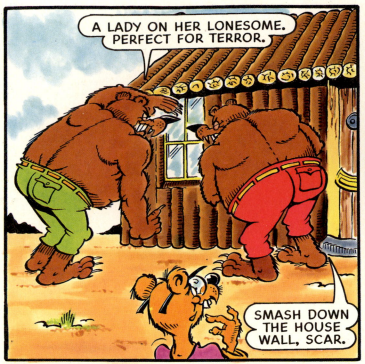

CUDDLES AND DIMPLES

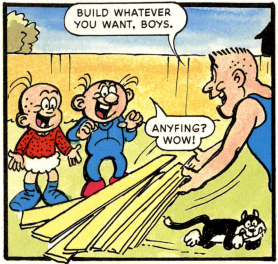

Bully Beef & Chips

A DESPERATE DAN MOVIE

SMASHER'S

(SMASHER MINIMUS)

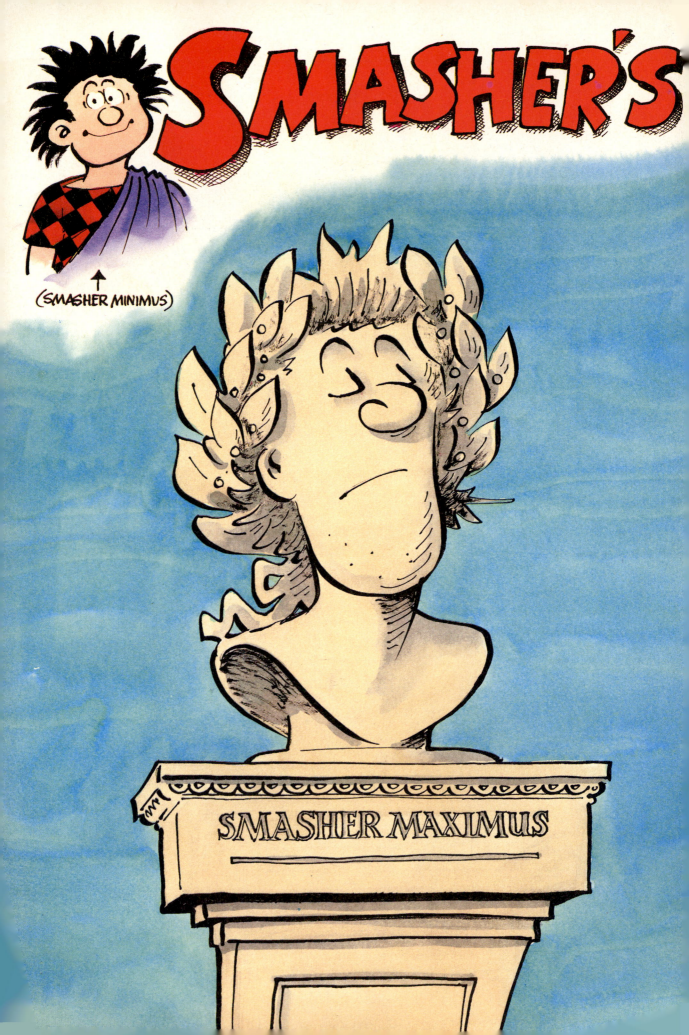

SMASHER MAXIMUS

ROMAN BUST-UP!

SMITTEN

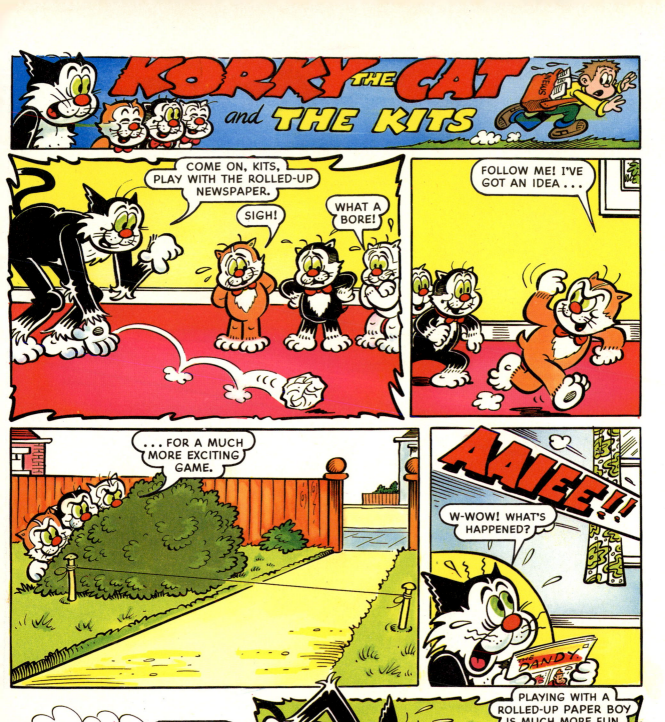
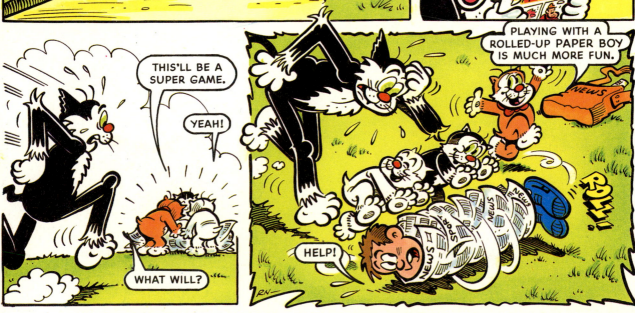

WINKER WATSON

HMM... WATSON AND HIS CRONIES ARE UP TO SOMETHING. IF ONLY I KNEW WHAT IT WAS.

IF ONLY I HAD A SPY IN THEIR MIDSTS, SOMEONE THEY'D NEVER SUSPECT... HMM...

JAMES BLOND SUPER SPY!

EUREKA!! I KNOW JUST THE LAD FOR THIS MISSION!

CUTHBERT? IT'S YOUR UNCLE CLARENCE HERE. I NEED YOUR HELP, MY BOY.

A few days later—

PAY ATTENTION, THIRD FORM. WE HAVE A NEW BOY JOINING US TODAY.

I'D LIKE YOU ALL TO MEET CUTHBERT CREE... ER, CRINGE. CUTHBERT CRINGE.

3RD FORM

HMM. LOOKS FAMILIAR.

THEY DUG A TUNNEL UNDER A VAULTING HORSE AND ESCAPED.

AND GUESS WHO HAVE GAMES BEFORE THEIR BIG FRENCH TEST TOMORROW MORNING...

And—

HA! THEY'RE TELLING HIM EVERYTHING. WHAT A BRILLIANT PLAN! WHAT A CLEVER CREEP YOU ARE!

SO YOU'LL DO IT?

YOU CAN TRUST ME, WINKER. I PROMISE.

DO YOU TRUST HIM, WINKER?

DON'T WORRY, LADS. I'VE GOT IT ALL UNDER CONTROL.

Have you really, Winker?

THEY'RE PLANNING TO TUNNEL OUT BEFORE THE EXAM. WATSON TOLD ME SO.

FINALLY, I'VE OUTWITTED HIM! I'LL CATCH HIM RED HANDED AND SEE HIM EXPELLED FOR THIS!

MR. CREEP

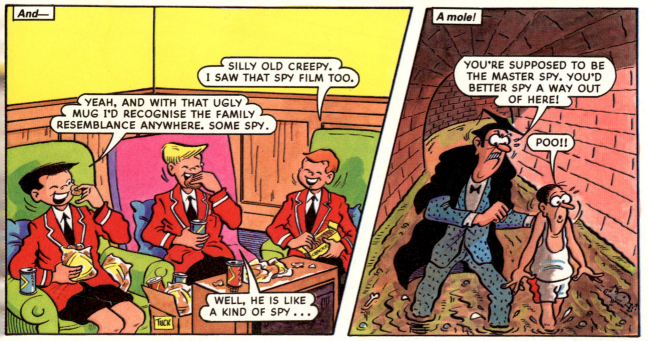

GROWING PAYNES

Later —

DAD! TELL THE PLANE TO STOP, I NEED TO GO.

THERE'S A TOILET BACK HERE.

TOILET

WON'T PEA LONG, DAD.

OKAY! I'LL WAIT OUT HERE.

Much later —

TOILET

GET A MOVE ON.

TELL THE BRAT TO HURRY UP.

HE'S BEEN IN THERE FOR AGES!

OH, DEAR!

PERCY! ARE YOU READY YET? PEOPLE ARE NEEDING IN.

TOILET

COMING, DAD!

TAP!

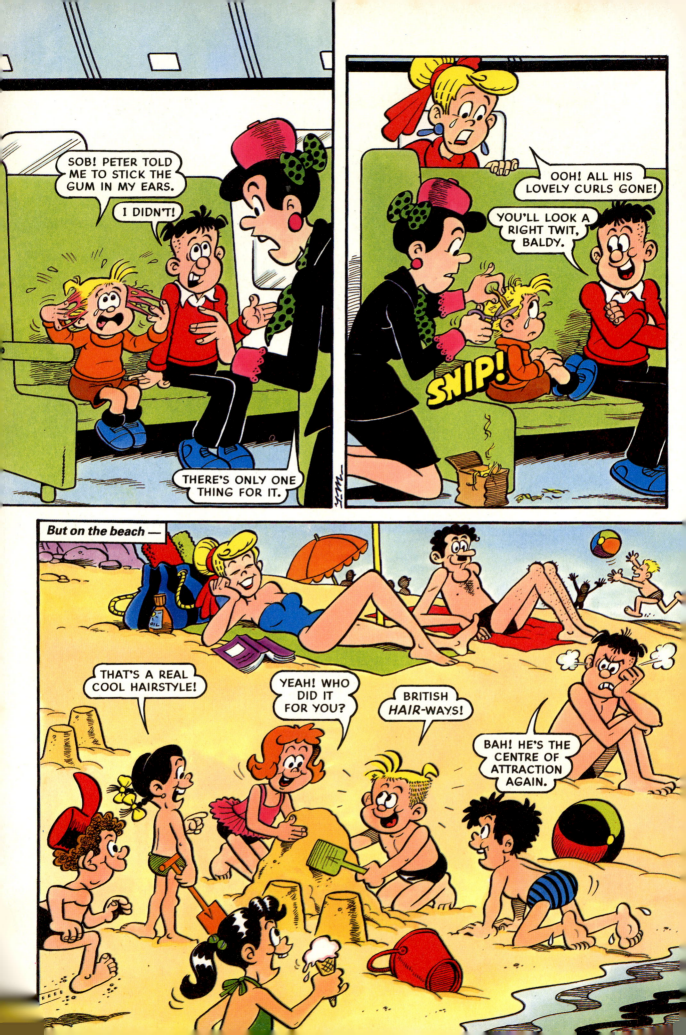

So —

The rov[...]

THAT'S BETTER! NOW TO USE SOME OF THE MACHINES.

SWEAT!!

GNNNGH!

GMMMPH!

The cycling machine —

And, the sorest of them all —

C'MON, THEN! STRETCH THOSE EXPANDERS!

TWANG!!

TINGG!

BOOINGG

STRETCH! STRETCH! STRETCH!

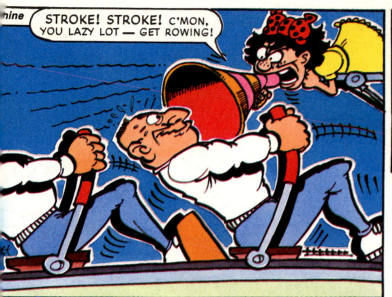

STROKE! STROKE! C'MON, YOU LAZY LOT — GET ROWING!

Weights —

THESE WEIGHTS ARE EASY!

C'MON! PUT A BIT OF EFFORT IN OR I'LL NEVER GET FIT!

The running machine —

PIECE OF CAKE WITH A SKATEBOARD!

SNAP!

THAT'S IT! WE'VE HAD ENOUGH!

EEAARGH!

HUH! JUST CAN'T GET THE LABOUR THESE DAYS.

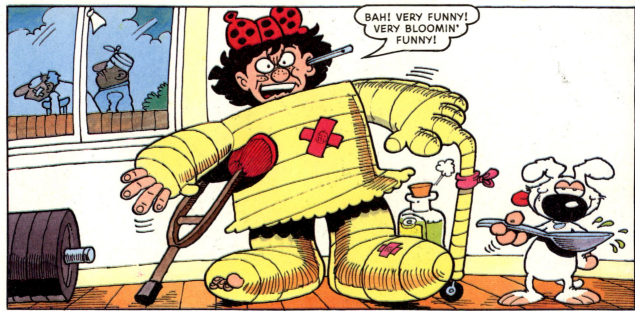

teddy
SCISSORHANDS
DANDY
PRODUCTIONS
NOW SHOWING AT CACTUSVILLE ODEON!
A DESPERATE DAN MOVIE

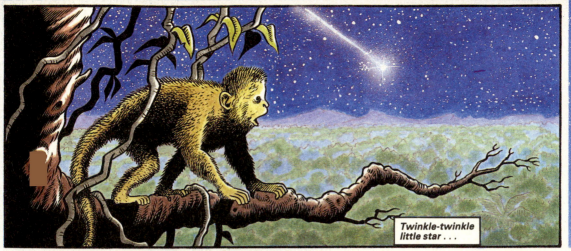

Twinkle-twinkle
little star . . .

How I wonder
what you are.

An Amazonian rain forest a year from now,
is about to greet a visitor.

A visitor who has travelled
a long way . . .

BREATHABLE ATMOSPHERE,
AT LONG LAST.

Unfortunately the forest has more than one visitor!

YOU CAN'T STAND IN THE WAY OF PROGRESS, OLD MAN. THE PAN-GLAX CORPORATION OWNS THIS FOREST NOW!

AND IF YOUR PEOPLE AREN'T AWAY FROM HERE BY SUNDOWN YOU WILL BE BULLDOZED ALONG WITH THOSE WORTHLESS TREES!

SO I WAS RIGHT! THEY ARE HERE!

WHERE WILL WE GO, GRANDPOPPA?

THERE IS NOWHERE FOR US TO GO, BOY. THIS IS OUR HOME!

HAH! THE PATHETIC FOOLS! TONIGHT WE STRIKE!

AND I'LL BE READY FOR YOU!

That night, as the village sleeps . . .

IT'S THEM! THEY'VE STARTED ALREADY!

Bellowing like enraged, red-eyed monsters, the bulldozers begin their deadly onslaught.

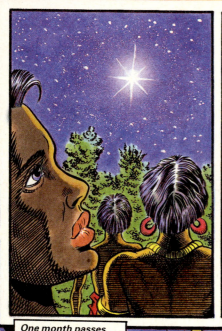

I AM SO SORRY ABOUT YOUR VILLAGE. I CAN'T . . .

PLEASE . . . DO NOT WORRY. WE CAN REBUILD. AT LEAST THE FOREST STILL STANDS.

THE SNAKE-HEAD CALLED YOU PRINCESS!

WE WOULD BE HONOURED IF YOU WOULD JOIN OUR TRIBE, AMAZON WARRIOR.

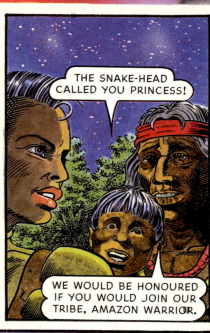

One month passes . . .

NO SIGN YET, BUT THE PAN-GLAXICANS WILL NOT ACCEPT DEFEAT EASILY.

Twinkle-twinkle little star . . .

AND I'LL BE WAITING FOR THEM!

How I wonder what you are.

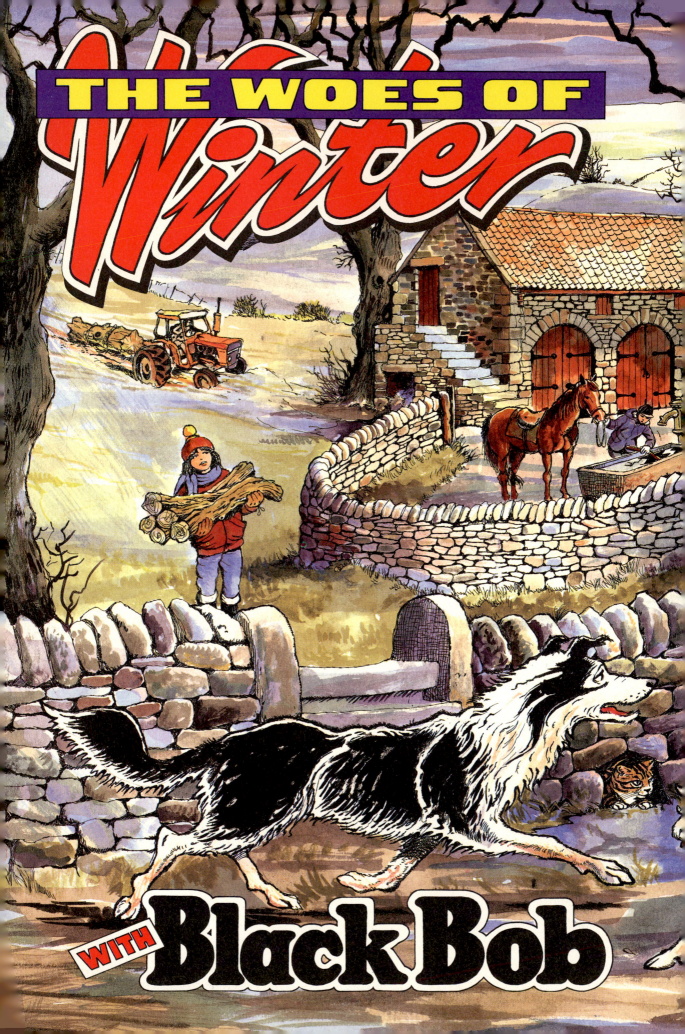

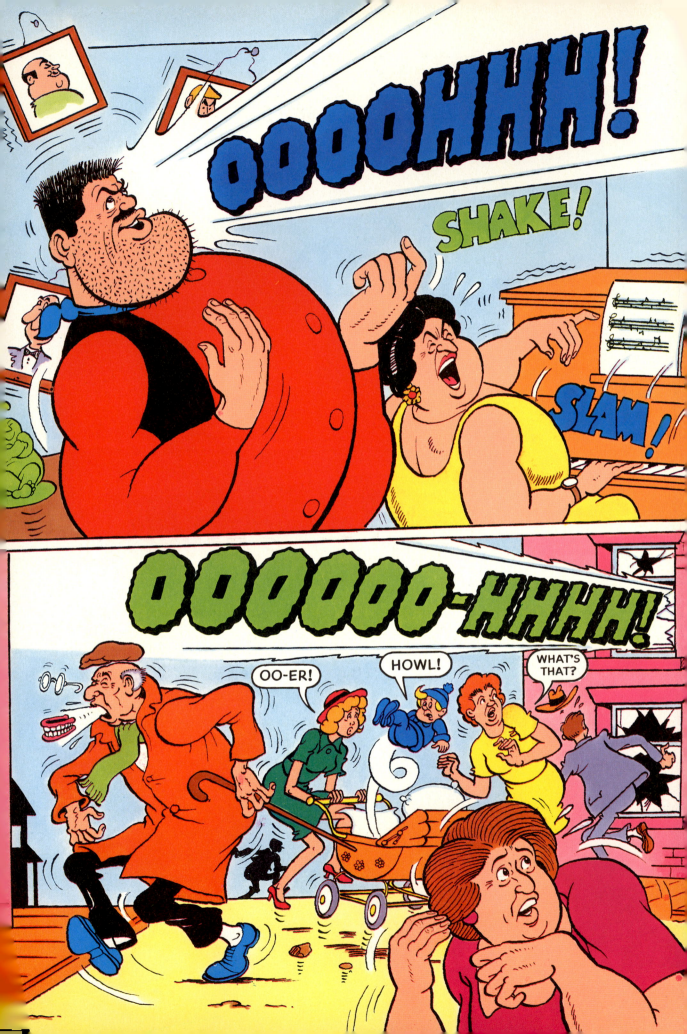

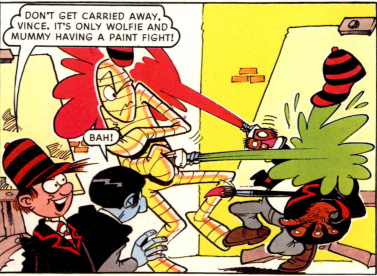

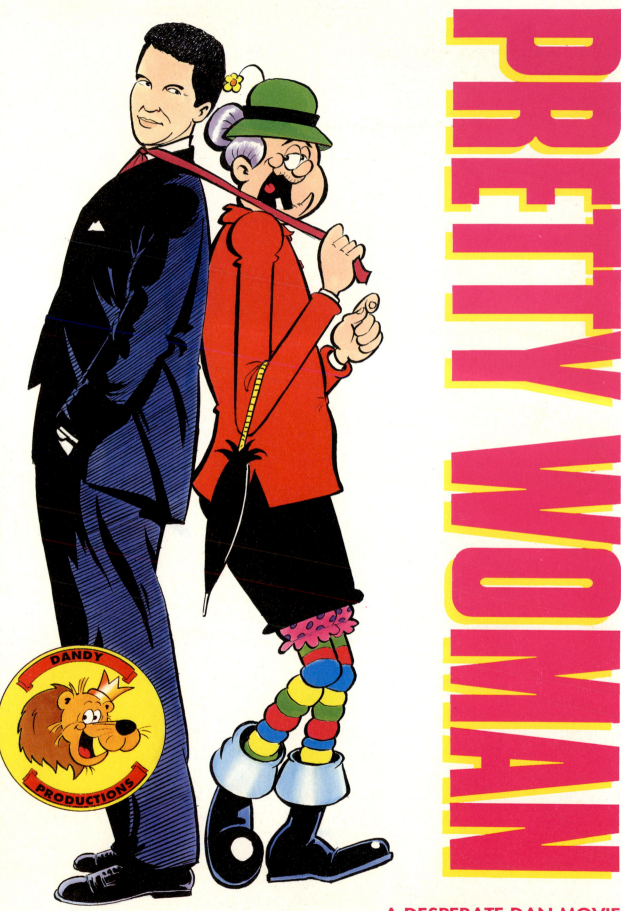

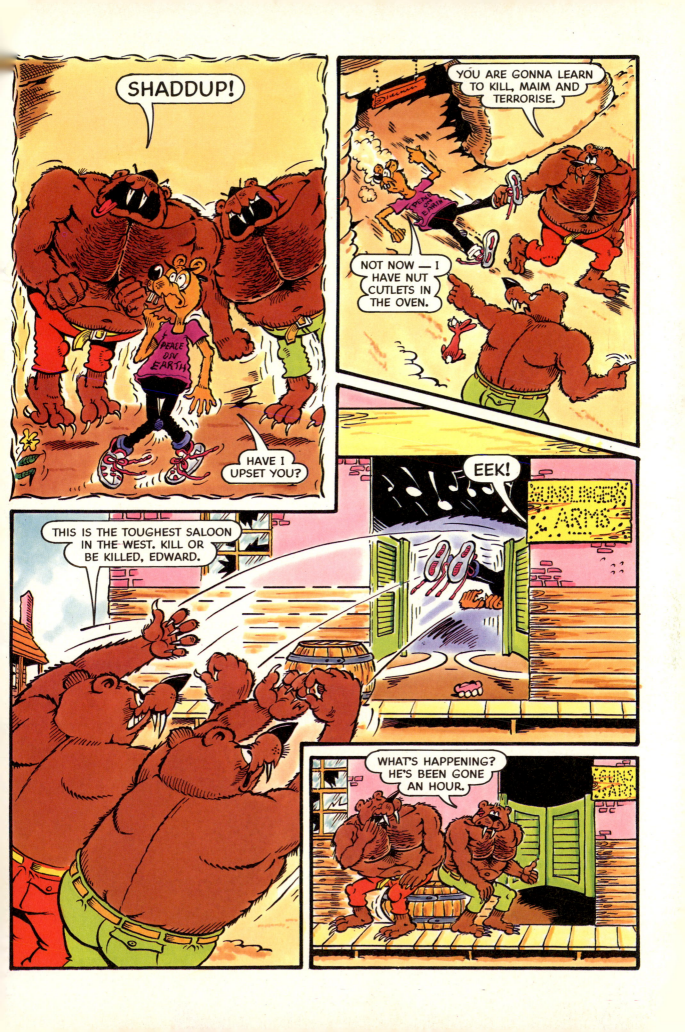

BILLY GREEN and his Sister Jean

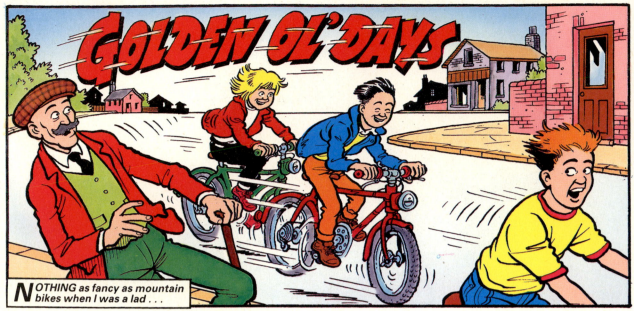

GOLDEN OL' DAYS

NOTHING as fancy as mountain bikes when I was a lad . . .

. . . carties were the thing and what races we had.

Pram wheels made your cartie like a Rolls Royce — but they cost a bit . . .

. . . but there were cheaper wheels — wooden ones from the saw-mill.

SAWMILL

Wooden wheels rattled your bones a bit — and could never out-run the smooth-running pram wheels or "coachers" as some called them.

OOFYAH!

KERASH!

. . . and they were easily broken. However . . .

. . . you could earn a bob or two by selling the bits for firewood . . .

. . . and buy a set of pram wheels from the local scrappies!

SCRAPYARD

YIPPEE! LOOK WHO'S WINNING NOW!

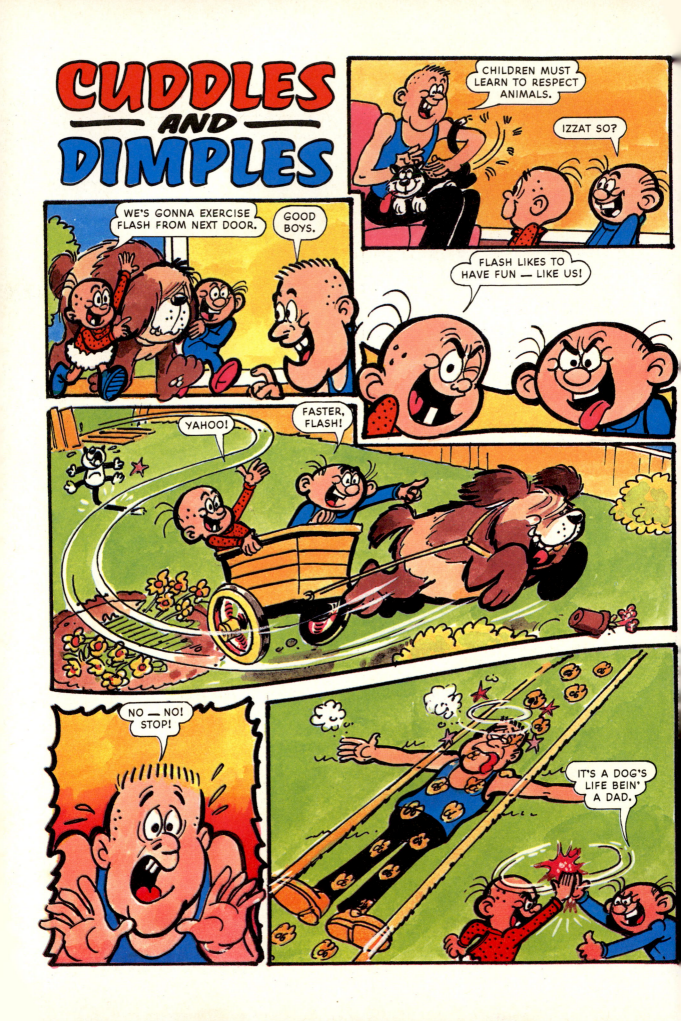

CHUG·A·CHUG!

DRRRR

DRRRR

ROAD UP

OOH! AND SOME WORKER DIGGING UP THE ROAD.

THERE'S JUST ONE THING FOR IT.

AND WHAT'S THAT, BILLY?

WE'RE TAKING TO THE HILLS. GET YOUR GEAR PACKED.

THUD!

AARGH!

I ALWAYS GO PREPARED. HAVE YOU GOT YOUR WATERPROOFS? YOUR SUN-TAN LOTION? CLEAN SOCKS?

...ALONG THE MOUNTAIN TRACK.

OH, NO! AN 'ORRIBLE 'UMAN!

MAKE A FOOL OF ME, EH? TAKE THAT!

PRONG!

GLOOMPH!

PUTRID POND

NASTY NIFF

I HOPE BILLY PACKED SOMETHING FOR THIS EMERGENCY.

'ORRIBLE ODOUR

GREAT! ALWAYS REMEMBER TO PACK A GAS-MASK WHEN YOU'RE HILL-WALKING.

THERE! WITH MY KEYHOLE AND CEDRIC'S KEY, THE GATES WILL OPEN.

WELL DONE! AND WE'RE JUST IN TIME FOR TEA.

Later—

SO THERE YOU HAVE IT, THAT'S HOW THE KEYHOLE WAS INVENTED. AND EVEN TODAY MY DESCENDANT, KATE, LOVES THEM...

Down in Dandyville—

WHAT A LOVELY DAY FOR KEYHOLE PEEPING. YUMMY!

...BUT SOMETIMES SHE OVERDOES IT!

HOW DID THAT HAPPEN? FORECAST SAID IT WOULD BE SUNNY ALL DAY!

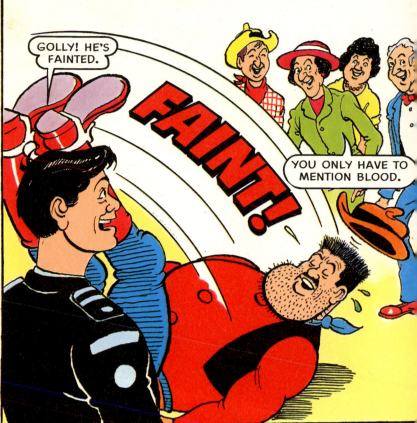